A QUATERMAIN A

KING SOLOMON'S MINES

By MARK ELLIS
&
PABLO MARCOS

Adapted from the novel by
H. Rider Haggard

CLASSICS
REIMAGINED

FOR **MARKOSIA ENTERPRISES** LTD

HARRY MARKOS
PUBLISHER & MANAGING PARTNER

GM JORDAN
SPECIAL PROJECTS CO-ORDINATOR

ANNIKA EADE
MEDIA MANAGER

ANDY BRIGGS
CREATIVE CONSULTANT

MEIRION JONES
MARKETING DIRECTOR

IAN SHARMAN
EDITOR IN CHIEF

ISBN 978-1-915387-08-0

www.markosia.com

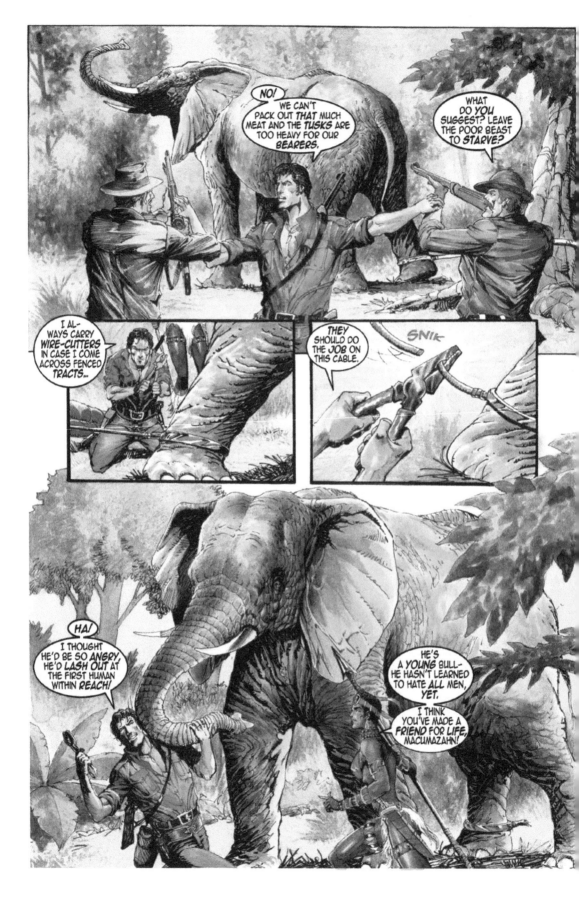

In 1997, Pablo Marcos illustrated a condensed version of *King Solomon's Mines*, published by Baronet Books as part of their Great Illustrated Classics series for young readers.

On the following pages are selected illustrations from the Baronet Books edition, juxtaposed with the same scenes depicted in the graphic novel.

AND SPEAKING OF SILVESTRE...

Early character
studies of
Quatermain and
Ignosa
by

Pablo's preliminary sketch of the cover...

...And the completed version.

Pablo's pencil layouts for page 42...

...And the finished version.

RICHARD SOON LEARNED THAT NATIVE SECRETS WERE TABOO! THERE WERE FREQUENT FIST AND KNIFE FIGHTS AGAINST WOULD-BE ASSASSINS -- AND HIS ALMOST DAILY BATTLES SOON EARNED HIM AN APPROPRIATE NICKNAME!

THERE GOES *RUFFIAN DICK* AGAIN -- AND THAT'S THE THIRD BRAWL HE'S BEEN IN TODAY!

AFTER TEN YEARS OF ADVENTURING IN INDIA, RICHARD SPEND A *WELL-EARNED* FURLOUGH AT BOULOGNE, WHERE HE MET ISABEL ARUNDEL, THE GIRL WHO WAS TO SPUR HIM ON TO EVEN *GREATER* ADVENTURES.

GREAT SCOTT -- THAT'S THE LOVELIEST GIRL I'VE EVER SEEN! I'VE GOT TO ATTRACT HER ATTENTION *SOME* WAY!

OHHH!

I LOVE YOU, WHEN CAN I SEE YOU AGAIN?

CAPTIVATED BY THE HANDSOME RICHARD'S BOLDNESS, ISABEL FELL MADLY IN LOVE WITH HIM -- BUT ALTHOUGH SHE ACCEPTED THE YOUNG ADVENTURER'S PROPOSAL OF MARRIAGE...

OURS IS AN ILLUSTRIOUS FAMILY -- AND YOU ARE PENNILESS, UNKNOWN! ONLY WHEN YOU'VE MADE A *NAME* FOR YOURSELF WILL I LET YOU MARRY ISABEL!

THERE'S ONLY ONE KIND OF REPUTATION I WANT -- THAT OF A *SOLDIER OF FORTUNE!* AND THE QUICKEST WAY TO BECOME FAMOUS IS TO DO THE ONE THING NO ENGLISHMAN HAS *EVER* YET DONE -- VISIT THE FORBIDDEN CITY OF MECCA AND OBSERVE THE SACRED MOSLEM CEREMONIES AT THE BLACK STONE OF THE KAABA! MY NAME WILL GO DOWN IN HISTORY IF I CAN DO THAT AND *LIVE!*

BUT -- BUT YOU'LL BE RISKING YOUR LIFE!

STAINING HIS FACE BROWN WITH WALNUT JUICE, RICHARD SET SAIL FROM ENGLAND IN APRIL OF 1853 -- AND AT CAIRO, THERE DISEMBARKED A MOSLEM BY THE NAME OF MIRZA ABDULLAH OF BUSHIRI -- ALIAS *RUFFIAN DICK!*

SO PERFECT WAS HIS DISGUISE, SO WELL HAD HE VERSED HIMSELF IN THE ARABIC LANGUAGE AND RELIGION, THAT HE WAS ABLE TO PERFORM THE CEREMONIAL RELIGIOUS RITES NIGHT AND MORNING WITHOUT BEING DETECTED!

HEARING OF A CARAVAN OF ARAB PILGRIMS HEADED FOR THE HOLY CITY OF MECCA, RICHARD BEGAN THE LONG TREK THROUGH THE BURNING DESERTS OF ARABIA! HE WAS UNNOTICED, IGNORED AS MERELY ANOTHER PIOUS MOSLEM—UNTIL ONE DAY JUST BEYOND EL HAMRA—

TO ARMS! —THE BEDOUINS ARE ATTACKING!

IN THE ENSUING FIERCE BATTLE, THE BEDOUINS SOON FOUND OUT THAT MIRZA ABDULLAH OF BUSHIRI WIELDED A MIGHTY SWORD!

LET US FLEE -- WE CANNOT FIGHT AGAINST SUCH A SWORDSMAN!

MIRZA ABDULLAH HAS SAVED US! MAY ALLAH SMILE UPON HIM ALL THE DAYS OF HIS LIFE!

THEN **MECCA**, THE HOLY CITY OF ISLAM—AND THE SACRED BLACK STONE OF THE KAABA, HOLIEST RELIC OF MOHAMMED-ANISM!

I'VE DONE IT--I'M THE FIRST OUTSIDER EVER TO PARTICIPATE IN THE RITES OF THE KAABA. IT WOULD MEAN MY HEAD IF THEY EVER FOUND OUT I'M AN ENGLISHMAN!

BUT HAVING ONCE TASTED THE THRILL OF ENTERING A FORBIDDEN CITY, RICHARD HAD AN OVERPOWERING DESIRE TO EXPLORE THE MOST FORBIDDEN CITY OF ALL — THE GOLDEN CITY OF HARAR IN SOMALILAND, WHICH NO WHITE MAN HAD EVER SEEN BEFORE!

THE SOMALIS ARE THE FIERCEST TRIBESMEN IN AFRICA — YOU'LL NEVER GET TO HARAR ALIVE!

YOU MAKE IT SOUND FASCINATING TO A SOLDIER OF FORTUNE!

IN THE COMPANY OF THREE ARAB ADVENTURERS, AND HIMSELF DISGUISED AS A HAJI MOSLEM MERCHANT, RICHARD BEGAN HIS SAFARI, PLUNGING EVER DEEPER INTO THE WILDS OF UNEXPLORED SOMALILAND! ADVENTURE WASN'T LONG IN COMING --

SOMALIS! SHOOT THEM!

NO — WE'D ONLY INCUR THE ENMITY OF THE WHOLE SOMALI NATION! IF I CAN ONLY TERRIFY THEM WITHOUT KILLING ANY OF THEM --

3

SPOTTING A FLIGHT OF VULTURES AHEAD, RICHARD IMPERTURBABLY FIRED AT **THEM** INSTEAD OF AT THE SOMALIS.'

YIII--- HE WHO CAN BRING THE VULTURES DOWN FROM THE SKIES MUST BE A **GOD!**

BANG! BANG

BUT THERE WERE STILL OTHER DANGERS TO BE FACED ON THE LONG TREK--FOR SOMALILAND WAS NOTORIOUS LION COUNTRY! AGAIN AND AGAIN THE ADVENTURER WAS CALLED UPON TO USE HIS COOL HEAD AND ACCURATE EYE TO SAVE HIS NECK!

BANG!

WORD OF HIS PROWESS SPREAD LIKE WILDFIRE THROUGH THE NATIVE VILLAGES! MANY OF THE LOCAL CHIEFS TRIED TO MARRY THEIR DAUGHTERS OFF TO THIS MIGHTY WARRIOR!

YOU MARRY DAUGHTER -- OR YOU **DIE!**

GUESS AGAIN!

SO LONG, CHIEF -- HOPE YOU HAVE MORE SUCCESS WITH THE **NEXT** MAN YOU PICK FOR A SON-IN-LAW!

AND THEN, THE MYSTERIOUS CITY OF HARAR -- UNTROD BY THE FOOT OF CIVILIZED MAN!

SORRY, OLD CHAP--- BUT I'LL NEED YOUR UNIFORM TO GET BEYOND THE WALLS OF HARAR!

ONCE INSIDE THE EXOTIC CITY, THE DISGUISED ADVENTURER HAD A PROBLEM! HOW TO MEET THE **GRAND EMIR OF HARAR**-- MOST FEARED RULER OF ALL AFRICA? FINALLY---

HMM, A **COBRA!** AND THAT GIVES ME AN **IDEA!**

WHEN THE GRAND EMIR PASSED ON HIS DAILY ROUNDS OF THE CITY'S DEFENSES, RICHARD POSTED HIMSELF NEARBY -- AND STEALTHILY TIPPED OVER THE BASKET CONTAINING THE VENOMOUS COBRA!

COBRA!

4

THE SERPENT MIGHT HAVE STRUCK AT ME IF NOT FOR THAT GUARD'S BRAVERY!

SWISH!

I HEREBY APPOINT YOU AS CAPTAIN OF MY GUARDS!

MY THANKS, O MIGHTY EMIR!

THE SOLDIER OF FORTUNE LEFT HARAR BEFORE HIS DECEPTION WAS DISCOVERED AND RETURNED TO BERBERAH TO PREPARE FOR ANOTHER EXPEDITION INTO THE HEART OF DARKEST AFRICA—THIS TIME WITH THE AID OF TWO BRITISH ARMY MEN! BUT AT 2 A.M. ON APRIL 17, 1856—

SHOTS! RICHARD—WAKE UP!

I'M UP—SOUNDS LIKE A BIT OF JOLLY FUN OUTSIDE! LET'S JOIN IN!

BANG! BANG! BANG!

BY GEORGE—A SOMALI RAID!

HMM, SEEMS TO BE OVER 350 OF THE BLIGHTERS—JUST ABOUT THE RIGHT ODDS FOR THREE ENGLISHMEN!

WE'RE DROPPING THEM LIKE FLIES—BUT THEY STILL KEEP COMING ON! WE'D BETTER SEPARATE AND MAKE A RUN FOR IT!

BANG! BANG! BANG!

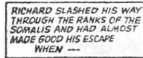

RICHARD SLASHED HIS WAY THROUGH THE RANKS OF THE SOMALIS AND HAD ALMOST MADE GOOD HIS ESCAPE WHEN —

WITHOUT HESITATING, RUFFIAN DICK TORE LOOSE THE SPEAR—AND DELIVERED A DEATH BLOW!

5

BUT WHEN RICHARD RETURNED TO ENGLAND, CERTAIN THAT THE NEWS OF HIS FAMED AFRICAN EXPLOITS WOULD ENABLE HIM TO CLAIM THE GIRL HE LOVED...

YOU'VE ACHIEVED A CERTAIN REPUTATION AS A FIGHTER AND AN ADVENTURER -- BUT THAT ISN'T WHAT I WANT MY SON-IN-LAW TO BE! BUT IF YOU COULD ONLY BECOME FAMOUS AS A REPUTABLE *EXPLORER* -- SOMEONE WHO'S RECOGNIZED BY THE ROYAL GEOGRAPHICAL SOCIETY...

IF I DON'T--IT WON'T BE FOR THE LACK OF TRYING!

RICHARD IMMEDIATELY MADE HIS PLANS AND LAID THEM BEFORE THE ROYAL GEOGRAPHICAL SOCIETY!

I'M THE ONLY MAN WHO KNOWS ENOUGH ABOUT AFRICA'S INTERIOR TO VERIFY NATIVE RUMORS ABOUT A HUGE BODY OF WATER IN THE UJIJI AREA! IF THERE *IS* SUCH A GREAT LAKE, *I'LL FIND IT!*

FROM WHAT WE'VE HEARD ABOUT YOUR EXPLOITS, SIR, WE'RE SURE YOU WILL! WE'LL GIVE YOU FINANCIAL BACKING AND APPOINT YOU AS THE LEADER OF AN EXPEDITION!

THE EXPEDITION DISEMBARKED AT ZANZIBAR ON DECEMBER 19, 1856! AND THEN THERE BEGAN A LONG, TORTUOUS TREK THROUGH JUNGLES AND ACROSS DESERTS--CONTINUALLY BESET BY NATIVE TRIBES WHO FEARED THE ENGLISHMEN WERE SLAVE-TRADERS!

EVEN THE ARAB SLAVE-TRADERS THEMSELVES THOUGHT THE EXPEDITION HAD COME TO ENCROACH ON THEIR TERRITORY, AND THE EXPLORER'S SMALL BAND HAD TO FIGHT OFF CONSTANT RAIDS FROM ALL SIDES!

BUT FINALLY, ON FEBRUARY 13, 1857, RICHARD BURTON ENJOYED THE GREATEST DAY OF HIS LIFE AS HE BECAME THE FIRST WHITE MAN TO LOOK DOWN UPON THE GREAT LAKE OF UJIJI--LATER TO BE KNOWN AS *TANGANYIKA!*

THE SOLDIER OF FORTUNE RETURNED TO ENGLAND WHERE HIS MAGNIFICENT ACHIEVEMENT EARNED HIM WORLD-WIDE HONORS AND RECOGNITION-- AND ALSO *THE GIRL OF HIS DREAMS!*

The END

HENRY MORTON STANLEY... the ADVENTUROUS SCRIBE

WHEN HENRY MORTON STANLEY LEFT HIS HOME IN LIVERPOOL TO SAIL TO NEW ORLEANS AS A CABIN BOY IN 1859, HE EMBARKED UPON A LIFE OF ADVENTURE! AFTER SEEING ACTION IN THE CIVIL WAR HE TRAVELED THE GREAT WESTERN PLAINS OF THE UNITED STATES, AND HIS GIFTS FOR DESCRIPTIVE WRITING BROUGHT HIM A WORLD-WIDE ROVING ASSIGNMENT FOR THE NEW YORK HERALD. RETURNING FROM A MISSION IN ABYSSINIA IN 1870, HE WAS SENT FOR BY HIS PUBLISHER, GORDON BENNETT, JR......

HENRY, THIS IS THE MOST IMPORTANT ASSIGNMENT OF YOUR CAREER! DR. DAVID LIVINGSTONE, THE FAMOUS EXPLORER, IS SOMEWHERE IN AFRICA! HE'S BEEN LOST FOR MORE THAN THREE YEARS! *YOU MUST FIND HIM!*

BUT AFRICA IS ENORMOUS, MR. BENNETT! I WOULDN'T KNOW WHERE TO START! WHY ASK ME WHEN TWO SEARCH EXPEDITIONS HAVE ALREADY FAILED?

I HAVE THE UTMOST CONFIDENCE IN YOU, HENRY! YOU'VE DONE A GREAT JOB IN ABYSSINIA! YOU'RE THE **ONLY** MAN FOR THIS ASSIGNMENT!

ALL RIGHT, SIR, I'LL GO! IF DR. LIVINGSTONE CAN BE FOUND, I'LL FIND HIM!

STANLEY LEFT FOR THE DARK CONTINENT, AND ARRIVING IN ZANZIBAR, WAS FORCED TO WAIT MONTHS FOR THE RAINY SEASON TO END!

SELIM, TOMORROW WE SAIL FOR THE COAST! I'M SICK AND TIRED OF WAITING FOR THE RAINS TO END!

AS YOU WISH, MASTER! I WILL MAKE PREPARATIONS!

APRIL, 1871, IN THE INTERIOR OF TANGANYIKA

TANGANYIKA IS SO HUGE! WE NEED NATIVE GUIDES! LET'S TRY THAT VILLAGE!

GOOD! PERHAPS THEY MAY EVEN HAVE SEEN THE OLD DOCTOR!

OUR TRADERS GO DEEP INTO THE INTERIOR! YES, WE HAVE HEARD OF AN OLD WHITE-BEARDED MAN NEAR THE GREAT LAKE!

THAT'S GOOD NEWS! NOW, IF YOU WILL SUPPLY ME WITH SOME NATIVE GUIDES, I'LL PUSH ON!

MONTHS LATER THE PARTY HAD MOVED HUNDREDS OF MILES FURTHER WEST...

WE'VE COME EIGHT HUNDRED MILES AND LOST HALF OF OUR PARTY! AND NOW THIS IS LAKE TANGANYIKA! I DOUBT WHETHER ANYBODY IS WITHIN A HUNDRED MILES OF HERE!

BWANA, I KNOW VILLAGE UJIJI! NOT FAR! WE COME ALONG SOON!

THE OUTSKIRTS OF UJIJI WERE REACHED IN NOVEMBER, 1871...

I SEE DOCTOR, BUT HE NO BELIEVE YOU COME! HURRY, BWANA!

WE'LL FIND OUT SOON ENOUGH IF IT'S REALLY DR. LIVINGSTONE!

MOMENTS LATER THE FAMOUS MEETING TOOK PLACE...

DR. LIVINGSTONE, I PRESUME?

I THANK GOD THAT I HAVE BEEN PERMITTED TO SEE YOU, DOCTOR

AND WHEN THEY WERE ALONE ...

I'VE BEEN MOST FORTUNATE TO FIND YOU, DR. LIVINGSTONE! TWO EXPEDITIONS FAILED SINCE YOU'VE BEEN REPORTED LOST!

LOST? I'VE NEVER BEEN LOST! I WAS TOO ILL AND TOO WEAK TO TRAVEL! I COULDN'T GET LOST! I KNOW THIS COUNTRY!

AFTER EXPLORING LAKE TANGANY-IKA TOGETHER, STANLEY LEFT LIVINGSTONE TO BRING HIS REPORT TO THE WORLD...

WHEN YOU GET BACK TO LONDON, GIVE THESE JOURNALS TO MY MISSIONARY SOCIETY AS A SMALL TOKEN OF MY APPRECIATION!

I WILL, DOCTOR! BUT I CAN'T UNDERSTAND WHY YOU WANT TO REMAIN IN THIS COUNTRY!

IN LONDON, STANLEY'S MEETING WITH LIVINGSTONE WAS DOUBTED...

BUT WHAT PROOF DO YOU HAVE THAT YOU ACTUALLY MET DR. LIVINGSTONE, MR. STANLEY? YOU DIDN'T BRING HIM BACK!

HE DIDN'T WANT TO RETURN, BUT HERE IS DOCUMENTARY PROOF - DR. LIVINGSTONE'S JOURNAL!

GREAT HONOR WAS THEN HEAP-ED UPON STANLEY...

THIS IS A SMALL GIFT FOR THE COURAGEOUS EXPED-ITION YOU LED, MR. STANLEY! PLEASE ACCEPT IT ON BE-HALF OF THE BRITISH EMPIRE!

I AM DEEPLY HONORED, YOUR MAJESTY!

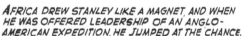

AFRICA DREW STANLEY LIKE A MAGNET, AND WHEN HE WAS OFFERED LEADERSHIP OF AN ANGLO-AMERICAN EXPEDITION, HE JUMPED AT THE CHANCE.

THESE MAPS ARE USELESS! I HEARD FROM LIVINGSTONE THAT THE CONGO FALLS ARE A HUNDRED MILES WEST OF HERE!

THEN LET'S GO, MR. STANLEY! I TRUST YOUR LEADERSHIP!

AND WHEN THEY REACHED THE GREAT FALLS...

NO WONDER LIVINGSTONE WAS STOPPED HERE! WE'LL NEVER GET PAST THESE FALLS WITH THAT SOLID ROCK IN THE WAY!

I'M NOT GOING TO LET THIS STOP ME FROM EXPLORING THE CONGO! WE'LL HACK OUR WAY THROUGH!

BWANA STANLEY, HE BULA MATARI, GREAT ROCK BREAKER!

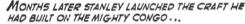

MONTHS LATER STANLEY LAUNCHED THE CRAFT HE HAD BUILT ON THE MIGHTY CONGO...

WE'VE ONLY BEGUN OUR EXPEDITION! THERE'S MORE THAN A THOUSAND MILES OF RIVER AND JUNGLE AHEAD! BUT WE'RE THE FIRST WHITE MEN WHO'VE EVER BEEN HERE!

THIS BLASTED HEAT AND THE FEVER ARE DECIMATING OUR RANKS, STANLEY! IT'LL BE A MIRACLE IF WE REACH THE COAST ALIVE!

TO ADD TO THEIR MANY OBSTACLES THEY WERE UNDER ATTACK BY HOSTILE TRIBES ALL ALONG THE ROUTE!

KEEP THE MEN PADDLING - OUR FIRE IS HOLDING THEM OFF!

YES, BUT WE'VE LOST TWO MORE BOAT LOADS!

A YEAR LATER...

I'M AFRAID I'M GOING, STANLEY, JUST LIKE OUR OTHER TWO COMRADES! REMEMBER ME TO... MY FAMILY!

HOLD ON, OLD MAN! DON'T LEAVE ME NOW! IT'S ONLY A FEW HUNDRED MILES!

WHEN STANLEY REACHED THE MOUTH OF THE CONGO, THREE YEARS HAD PASSED AND HE WAS THE LONE WHITE SURVIVOR...

GOOD HEAVENS! IT CAN'T BE! YOU WERE REPORTED DEAD TWO YEARS AGO! WHERE ARE THE REST OF YOUR PARTY, MR. STANLEY?

I CAME THROUGH ALONE! THE REST, GOOD BRAVE MEN, PERISHED ALONG THE ROUTE! BUT THE CONGO HAS BEEN CHARTED!

SEVEN YEARS LATER, AFTER HELPING ESTABLISH THE CONGO FREE STATE, STANLEY LED A BRITISH RESCUE MISSION FOR EMIN PASHA, GOVERNOR OF EQUATORIAL AFRICA...

IF I LEAVE, I WILL LOSE MY TERRITORY AND ALL MY RIGHTS!

AND IF YOU STAY YOU WILL BE DEAD! I CAME A THOUSAND MILES TO BRING YOU BACK, AND I'VE LOST HALF OF MY MEN! YOU'RE RETURNING WITH ME BY ORDERS OF THE CROWN!

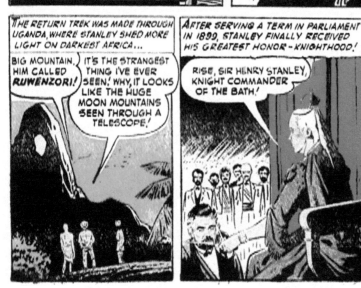

THE RETURN TREK WAS MADE THROUGH UGANDA, WHERE STANLEY SHED MORE LIGHT ON DARKEST AFRICA...

BIG MOUNTAIN, HIM CALLED RUWENZORI!

IT'S THE STRANGEST THING I'VE EVER SEEN! WHY, IT LOOKS LIKE THE HUGE MOON MOUNTAINS SEEN THROUGH A TELESCOPE!

AFTER SERVING A TERM IN PARLIAMENT IN 1899, STANLEY FINALLY RECEIVED HIS GREATEST HONOR - KNIGHTHOOD!

RISE, SIR HENRY STANLEY, KNIGHT COMMANDER OF THE BATH!

FIVE YEARS LATER THE INTREPID CONQUEROR OF THE DARK CONTINENT DIED AT HIS COUNTRY ESTATE IN PIRBRIGHT, MOURNED BY THE ENTIRE WORLD!

HENRY MORTON STANLEY
1841 - 1904
BULA MATARI
AFRICA

THE END

LOBENGULA

Who was he? The last of the great Zulu chiefs to fight the advance of the white invaders of Africa...*WHAT* was he? A symbol of primitive power, of raw courage in the face of overwhelming odds -- in short, a *MAN*!

Lobengula's boyhood is shrouded in mystery as dark as his Rhodesia jungle -- but he was certainly trained to perform the duties of a king --

As a young prince, he showed a wisdom rare in his people -- at last, the day came when Lobengula donned the crown of his powerful tribe, the Matabele --

We Zulus form many tribes with many kings -- thus, as a nation, we are *WEAK*!

Now we will make war on the white man!

I WILL NOT LEAD MY PEOPLE TO SLAUGHTER! WE MUST FIRST BE UNITED--**STRONG!**

HE IS NOT A GOOD KING -- HE HAS THE HEART OF A WOMAN!

MEANWHILE, CECIL RHODES, BRITISH EMPIRE BUILDER, LOOKED UPON LOBENGULA'S VAST COUNTRY WITH LONGING--

WE MUST GET THAT LAND--YET WE CANNOT RISK WAR WITH LOBENGULA!

WE MUST BE FAIR! TRY TO **BARGAIN** WITH HIM -- OFFER HIM GOLD IN EXCHANGE FOR HIS LAND!

SO-- TO LOBENGULA CAME WHITE TRADERS WHO SPOKE MUCH OF LAND, BOUNDARIES AND TREATIES IN LANGUAGE THAT THE BLACK KING DID NOT UNDERSTAND--

IN RETURN FOR THIS BAG OF GOLD, ALL I ASK IS YOUR SIGNATURE ON THIS PIECE OF PAPER!

THE NEXT TRADING MISSION TO THE LAND OF LOBENGULA WAS WARMLY WELCOMED -- IN BLOOD!

IT'S AN AMBUSH-- **BACK!**

YOUR TONGUE IS CROOKED! I HAVE SIGNED TOO MANY OF THESE SCRAPS OF PAPER-- AND THE GOLD IS ALL GONE!

2

BUT THE AMBUSH HAD BEEN PERFORMED WITHOUT LOBENGULA'S KNOWLEDGE...THE WARLIKE LEADERS WERE BOUND AND --

CUT OFF THEIR NOSES AND LIPS AND THROW THEM TO THE CROCODILES! WHEN BLOOD IS TO BE SPILLED, *I* WILL SPILL IT!

BY THIS ACT, YOU HAVE AVOIDED WAR WITH BRITAIN...YOU ARE A BRILLIANT STATESMAN, LOBENGULA!

BUT BY NOW, THE SETTLERS WERE CLAMORING FOR THE RICH LAND OF RHODESIA --

HOW CAN I PLEASE BOTH THE SETTLERS *AND* LOBENGULA - WITHOUT HALTING PROGRESS?

HE HAS SIGNED AN AGREEMENT ALLOWING SETTLERS IN HIS COUNTRY -- WELL, *SEND* THEM! IF HE ATTACKS, *HE* WILL BE RESPONSIBLE FOR THE RESULTING WAR!

THE SETTLERS COME! LET US ATTACK THEM -- DRIVE THEM BACK!

NO! THE BRITISH WOULD SEND THEIR ARMIES AGAINST US! OUR SPEARS ARE NO MATCH FOR THEIR GUNS!

BUT LOBENGULA COULD NOT CONTROL ALL OF HIS RESTLESS YOUNG WARRIORS --

YOU HAVE NO RIGHT! THIS IS MY LAND -- I HAVE PAPERS TO PROVE IT!

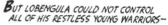

THE BRITISH HAVE YOU, LOBENGULA -- YOU HAVE LEGALLY *SOLD YOUR KINGDOM!*

IF THE BRITISH HAVE STOLEN MY KINGDOM LEGALLY, THEN I WILL KEEP IT -- *ILLEGALLY!* LET THEM FIGHT FOR IT!

NOT LONG AFTERWARD, CAME THE FINAL "INCIDENT" --

ONE OF LOBENGULA'S MEN -- IN OUR TERRITORY! SERVES HIM RIGHT!

3

MOUNTAINS OF THE MOON

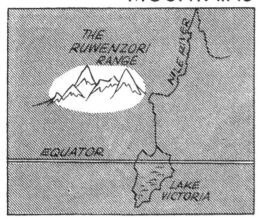

The Ruwenzori Range of mountains cover an area 80 miles long and 60 miles wide along Africa's hot equator, yet the mountain peaks are always covered with snow.

Nine peaks over 15,000 feet high and three peaks over 17,000 feet high rise into the sky. The people of Africa have long called these peaks the Mountains of the Moon.

The rugged mountains have many glaciers; and there the weather is always bad, with rain, fog and blizzards. Little grows on the steeps, few people venture into them.

However, on the slopes the temperature gets hotter and hotter on the way down, making an invariable hothouse, where giant ferns, huge bananas, and big flowers flourish.

In some areas bamboo grows so thick, it is almost impossible to penetrate it. In a day a shoot will grow as much as 18 inches, and in three months it will be 100 feet high.

The Mountains of the Moon is the birthplace of some streams that water the lowlands. The melting ice and snow flow partly into Lake Victoria and then into the Nile River.

THE JUNGLE PEOPLE

THE TOOTHY SMILE THIS **CROCODILE** IS FLASHING CAN BE FOUND IN MOST TROPICAL RIVERS ALL OVER THE WORLD! HE'S BIG, MEAN, AND ALWAYS HUNGRY, AND HE FEEDS ON MEAT! IF YOU'RE NOT *CAREFUL* NEAR A RIVER WHERE THEY'RE BROWSING, YOU'RE LIABLE TO BE THE MAIN COURSE! HE GROWS AS LONG AS TWENTY-FIVE FEET LONG! SOME SAY LONGER!

THE SNOW LEOPARD IS SAID TO BE THE MOST BEAUTIFUL OF ALL LEOPARDS BUT IT'S NOT A GOOD IDEA TO STAND AROUND ADMIRING HIM WHEN HE'S CHARGING! HE'S FOUND IN ASIA MOSTLY, WAY UP IN THE HILLS AND HE'S A TOUGH CUSTOMER!

THIS NOISY CHARACTER, THE **HOWLER MONKEY**, MAKES A LOT OF NOISE IN SOUTH AMERICA! THEY SIT UP IN THE TREETOPS AND TELL THE WORLD WHAT THEY THINK OF IT BUT NO ONE LISTENS MUCH!

THE Jungle People

THE LION MEASURES NINE TO TEN FEET FROM NOSE TO TIP OF TAIL, AND WEIGHS ABOUT 450 POUNDS! SO POWERFUL IS THIS KING OF AFRICAN CATS THAT A SINGLE BLOW OF HIS PAW CAN CRUSH AN OX'S SKULL! HE CAN JUMP 30 FEET IN A SINGLE LEAP! THE MANE GROWS ONLY ON THE MALE, BEGINNING DURING THE THIRD YEAR!

WHILE THE LION IS KING OF THE AFRICAN JUNGLE, THE TIGER, MOST VICIOUS OF THE BIG CATS, RULES OVER THE JUNGLES OF ASIA! THE TIGER IS LARGER AND MORE CUNNING THAN THE LION! HE SPANS ABOUT ELEVEN FEET AND WEIGHS ABOUT 500 POUNDS! THE ROYAL BENGAL TIGER IS FEARED THROUGHOUT ALL INDIA, AND FOR GOOD REASON: HE KILLS ALMOST A THOUSAND PEOPLE ANNUALLY THERE!

THE COMMON LEOPARD IS FAWN-COLORED, WITH DARK SPOTS! HE IS MUCH SMALLER THAN EITHER LION OR TIGER, MEASURING FOUR FEET IN BODY, WITH A THREE FOOT TAIL! THE LEOPARD IS LITHE AND AGILE, AND A FIERCE FOE WHEN CORNERED! UNLIKE LION AND TIGER, THE LEOPARD IS A TREE CLIMBER AND OFTEN POUNCES UPON HIS PREY FROM TREE BRANCHES!

THE Jungle People

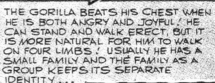

'THE GORILLA'

THE GORILLA IS THE LARGEST OF THE APES AND THE ANIMAL CLOSEST TO MAN HIMSELF! THE GORILLA LIVES PRINCIPALLY IN WEST AFRICA AND THE BELGIAN CONGO! THE FULL-GROWN MALE WEIGHS BETWEEN 400 AND 500 POUNDS! HE STANDS ABOUT 5 FEET HIGH! HIS STRENGTH IS ENORMOUS AND BECAUSE OF IT HE IS SELDOM MOLESTED BY OTHER ANIMALS...

THE GORILLA BEATS HIS CHEST WHEN HE IS BOTH ANGRY AND JOYFUL! HE CAN STAND AND WALK ERECT, BUT IT IS MORE NATURAL FOR HIM TO WALK ON FOUR LIMBS! USUALLY HE HAS A SMALL FAMILY AND THE FAMILY AS A GROUP KEEPS ITS SEPARATE IDENTITY...

IN SPITE OF HIS GREAT STRENGTH, THE GORILLA EATS NO MEAT, LIVES EXCLUSIVELY ON FRUITS AND VEGETABLES! THEREFORE HE IS NOT A HUNTER!

Jungle People
in 'JUNGLE PARTNERSHIP'

ALONG JUNGLE RIVERS AND LAKES GREAT NUMBERS OF CROCODILES LIVE AND NEST! THE SLUGGISH CROCODILE SLEEPS MUCH OF THE TIME AND IS SELDOM ALERT TO DANGER! THE HIPPOPOTAMUS, HOWEVER, IS CONSTANTLY ON THE LOOKOUT FOR ENEMIES, AND STANDS WATCH LIKE A HUGE MONITOR!

AT THE FIRST SOUND OF APPROACHING DANGER, THE MONITOR HIPPO LOWS LOUD AND LONG, WARNING OTHER HIPPOS, AND AT THE SAME TIME THE CROCODILES SLITHER AND DIVE INTO THE SAFETY OF THE WATER...

AS A REWARD FOR HIS SERVICES (EVEN THOUGH IT IS UNINTENTIONAL ON THE PART OF THE CROCODILE) THE HIPPOPOTAMUS DINES WELL ON CROCODILE EGGS OF WHICH HE IS VERY FOND! SINCE CROCODILES CONGREGATE IN LARGE NUMBERS, AND A SINGLE FEMALE CROCODILE LAYS 50 TO 60 EGGS, MR. HIPPO IS GENEROUSLY TREATED IN THIS STRANGE PARTNERSHIP!

THE JUNGLE PEOPLE

SIX TONS OF DESTRUCTION!

THE AFRICAN ELEPHANT IS THE LARGEST LAND DWELLING ANIMAL IN THE WORLD! THE HUNTER WHO IS UNFORTUNATE ENOUGH TO WOUND ONE OF THESE GIANTS GENERALLY NEVER GETS IN A SECOND SHOT! DESPITE HIS BULK, HE CAN MOVE AT TREMENDOUS SPEED! HIS TRUNK CAN DEMOLISH A NATIVE HUT OR EVEN TEAR UP SMALL TREES!

THE GEMSBOK!

THE GEMSBOK ACTUALLY IS AN ANTELOPE EVEN THOUGH HE LOOKS LIKE A WEIRD DREAM! HE CAN'T BE MISSED WITH THAT COLORING AND HE'S NOT BIG ENOUGH TO BE DANGEROUS—BUT THERE ARE REPORTS OF THE GEMSBOK BATTLING, AND KILLING, LIONS AND OTHER JUNGLE HUNTERS!

HE FLIES THROUGH THE AIR WITH THE GREATEST OF EASE!

THE GIBBON, A KIND OF APE, IS ONE OF THE FLYINGEST CHARACTERS TO BE FOUND! HE CAN COVER MORE THAN FORTY FEET IN ONE SWING! HE'S NOT MUCH FOR LOOKS BUT HE MORE THAN MAKES UP FOR IT IN AGILITY!

THE Jungle People

THE MOST DANGEROUS ANIMAL IN THE WORLD!

THE CAPE, OR WATER BUFFALO, HAS BEEN CALLED THE MOST VICIOUS, HARDEST TO KILL ANIMAL IN THE WORLD! WHEN WOUNDED, HE OFTEN WILL ABSORB A DOZEN HIGH POWERED BULLETS BEFORE GOING DOWN! WHITE HUNTERS TREAT HIM WITH CAREFUL RESPECT!

THE GIANT PANGOLIN!

THIS CRAZY LOOKING SPECIMEN LIVES ON ANTS AND TERMITES! HE'S ARMORED WITH SCALE-LIKE PLATES AND CAN DIG THROUGH CEMENT-HARD NESTS IN SECONDS! HE'S ABOUT FIVE FEET LONG AND ONE LOOK AT HIM IS MATERIAL ENOUGH FOR A MONTH-LONG NIGHTMARE!

REEDBUCK!

THE REEDBUCK IS A SOUTH AFRICAN ANTELOPE WHO TRAVELS ALONE AND AT HIGH SPEEDS! HE'S A PLAINS ANIMAL AND SPENDS MOST OF HIS TIME FIGHTING OFF LIONS TO PROTECT HIS FAMILY!

S757

THE JUNGLE PEOPLE

RHINO!

THE RHINOCEROS LOOKS LIKE AN EASY-GOING FELLOW--TILL HE GETS ANNOYED OR SMELLS THE HUNTER! THEN HE CHARGES LIKE A TANK AND IS TWICE AS HARD TO STOP! HE'S ON THE AGGRESSIVE SIDE AND HIS SENSE OF SMELL IS UNBELIEVABLE! HE'S A MIGHTY DANGEROUS ANIMAL!

ALMOST AN ELEPHANT!

THE TAPIR IS A PECULIAR MIXTURE OF ELEPHANT AND PIG! IT HAS A SNOUT THAT IS ALMOST A TRUNT BUT OTHERWISE IT LOOKS LIKE AN OVERGROWN PIG! IN MALAY, THE NATIVES REGUARD IT WITH AWE AND THE ONLY DANGER TO IT IS THE TIGER!

BACKWARDS BUT DANGEROUS!

THE WARTHOG IS A WILD PIG FOUND ON THE PLAINS OF AFRICA! WHEN ATTACKED, HE'LL RUN BUT NOT FAR, HE'LL FIND A HOLE AND BACK INTO IT, THUS HIS CURVED TUSKS OFFER A POTENT WEAPON AGAINST ANY ENEMY! EVEN A HUNGRY LION HAS LEARNED THAT THIS WILD PIG CAN BE A MIGHTY DANGEROUS FOE!

THE JUNGLE PEOPLE

GORILLA GONE MAD!

THE NATURALISTS TELL US THAT THE GORILLAS ARE USUALLY HAPPY TO MIND THEIR OWN BUSINESS AND BE LET ALONE! BUT THERE IS NOTHING IN THE JUNGLE MORE AWESOME THAN A FULL GROWN GORILLA WHO'S PEEVED AT A MAN! THEN THE STARTLING POUNDING ON THE CHEST BEGINS AND THE EARTH SHAKES, NOT TO MENTION THE KNEES OF THE HUNTER!

THE **ROCK JUMPER** OR **KLIPSPRINGER** IS A SMALL ANTELOPE THAT AFRICAN HUNTERS SAY CAN CLIMB STRAIGHT UP! THEY ALSO SAY HE CAN JUMP THIRTY FEET AND LAND WITH ALL FOUR HOOVES ON A ROCK AS BIG AS A MAN'S HAND! HE'S GOOD EATING FOR LIONS AND HUMANS ALIKE SO HE'S HUSTLING MOST OF THE TIME!

SCHNOZZOLA IS A LITTLE SENSITIVE ABOUT HIS SMELLER! KNOWN TO NATURALISTS AS THE PROBOSCIS MONKEY, HE DOESN'T HAVE A GOOD REASON FOR THE NASAL FACADE BUT WHO ARE NATURALISTS TO DECIDE THAT? AFTER ALL, HE MAY LOOK GOOD TO OTHERS OF HIS KIND SO WHAT DOES HE CARE!

THE JUNGLE PEOPLE

THE BLACK LEOPARD IS FOUND IN AFRICA AND ASIA! THE BLACK, A VARIATION OF THE SPOTTED LEOPARD, IS ONE OF THE DEADLIEST ANIMALS FOR ITS SIZE ANYWHERE! HE'S AS MUCH AT HOME JUMPING FROM TREE TO TREE AS HE IS ON THE GROUND! HE'S BEEN KNOWN TO FOLLOW A HUNTER IN THE TREES TILL HE DECIDES TO MAKE HIS LEAP!

THE MARMOSET AT FULL GROWTH, HE WEIGHS AROUND FOUR AND A HALF OUNCES! SOME LADIES BUY THEM FOR PETS AND KEEP THEM IN A POCKET! THEY COME FROM BRAZIL AND ARE EASILY TAMED!

THE MOOSE IS THE LARGEST DEER IN THE WORLD AND THE LARGEST ANIMAL IN NORTH AMERICA! THEY WEIGH ALMOST A TON AND STAND ABOUT SEVEN FEET TALL AT THE SHOULDERS! THEY LIVE MOST OF THEIR LIVES NEAR WATER AND SWIM EASILY, HAVING HOLLOW FUR HAIR THAT KEEPS THEM AFLOAT EASILY!

THE JUNGLE PEOPLE

THE CHACMA BABOON IS A CLIFF DWELLER FROM SOUTH AFRICA! A BIG ONE WILL WEIGH A HUNDRED AND FIFTY POUNDS AND EVERY POUND OF IT IS NASTY! THEY LIVE IN 'TOWNS' AND HUNTERS STAY AWAY FROM THEM! THEY LIVE ON SNAKES, LIZARDS, AND SCORPIONS WHICH PROBABLY IS WHY THEY'RE SO MEAN!

THE FLYING FOX IS A MEMBER OF THE BAT FAMILY! HE'S MORE THAN FOUR FEET FROM WING TO WING AND HAS A FACE LIKE A FOX! HANGS AROUND TREES IN THE MALAY PENINSULA AND GOES OUT AT NIGHT!

THE CHIMPANZEE IS AN APE! HE'S ONE OF THE MOST INTELLIGENT ANIMALS AROUND AND CAN RIDE BICYCLES, WEAR CLOTHES, USE A KNIFE AND FORK, ETC! A BIG MALE CHIMP RUNS ABOUT FIVE FEET HIGH AND WEIGHS AS MUCH AS A HUNDRED AND SEVENTY FIVE POUNDS!

AFRICAN BIRDS

THE **HORNBILLS** FEINT THEIR SNAKE VICTIM INTO STRIKING AT THEIR WINGTIPS. THEN WHEN THE SNAKE IS UNCOILED, THE BIRDS FINISH THE KILL WITH THEIR DEADLY BILLS.

THE **OSTRICH** IS OFTEN CALLED THE CAMEL BIRD, BECAUSE IT CAN GO WITHOUT WATER FOR A LONG TIME, BUT IT ENJOYS A DIP IN THE OCEAN, SOMETIMES UP TO ITS NECK.

THE SOUTH AFRICAN **WHITE-FRONTED BEE-EATER** HAS A ROYAL FEAST WHEN THE VELDT IS SWEPT BY FIRE. SWOOPING IN AND OUT OF THE FLAMES, THEY DEVOUR HORDES OF INSECTS THAT ARE STIRRED UP BY THE ADVANCING FIRE.

THE INDELICATE AFRICAN **VULTURES** HAVE THEIR SANITARY SIDE. AFTER THEIR DAILY BATH THEY PROCEED TO MANICURE THEIR BEAKS IN THE SAND AND THEN PREEN THEIR FEATHERS.

The TREE of LIFE

Growing like a great brooding giant in the midst of the almost impenetrable jungle, is the huge mis-shapen Baobab Tree! Its size is unbelievable, dwarfing men and beasts alike. But it is upon this tree that many natives depend for their very lives.

It often serves as a shelter as it is corroded with deep holes and tunnels, each big enough to hold at least a dozen men.

Its spongy trunk can be tapped for water, which it has soaked up and preserved for months.

From its bark can be made clothes, ropes, and even medicine. And its gourd-like fruits contain a tasty food, which the natives call "monkey bread."

SOUTH AFRICAN HEADDRESSES

THE **DODOTH** WARRIOR'S HELMET IS MADE BY MATTING HIS HAIR WITH CLAY AND DAUBING IT WITH PAINT AND THEN TOPPING IT OFF WITH AN OSTRICH PLUME. TO PRESERVE HIS COIFFURE AT NIGHT THE WARRIOR SLEEPS WITH HIS HEAD ON A STOOL.

THE **ZULU** WARRIOR OF SOUTH AFRICA WEARS AN ELABORATE HEADDRESS OF HORNS, FEATHERS, BEADS, WOOD AND FUR.

A **BORAN ELDER'S** HEADDRESS IS MADE OF ALUMINIUM. IN EARLIER DAYS THE ORNAMENT WAS MADE OF IVORY OR BRASS.

A **KUANYAMA** SPORTS AN ANIMAL MANE OF GIRAFFE OR GNU, ATTACHED TO A LEATHER HEADBAND. IT IS HELD IN PLACE WITH A CHIN STRAP.

THE **HERERO** OF THE TJIMBA TRIBE HAS A DOUBLE PIGTAIL OF PLAITED HAIR, DECORATED WITH TASSELS OF DAPHNE BERRIES.

THE **CAMEROUN CHIEF'S** HEADGEAR IS AN ORNATE ONE... A "WASP NEST" GLOBE SUPPORTED BY A STUFFED CROCODILE.

THE **LAST GOD-KING OF KAFFA**, GAKI SHEROCHO, WORE THIS SACRED GILT HEADDRESS AS HIS CROWN.

JUNGLE JUSTICE

COUNTER TO MODERN CREDENCE, JUNGLE JUSTICE IS NOT BASED ON "SURVIVAL OF THE FITTEST" OR "TO THE VICTOR GO THE SPOILS", BUT IS BASED ON MAN-MADE LAWS, RIGIDLY KEPT....

THE LEGAL KING-PIN IS THE EMIR'S APPOINTEE, CALLED AN "ALKALI", WHO DISPENSES JUSTICE IN THE MORE SERIOUS TRIALS...

BUT WHEN CHIEFS DO WRONG, THEY ARE TRIED BY THEIR OWN PEERS, AND SENTENCED BY THE TRIBAL KING, WHO MAY GRANT A PARDON BY A MERE EXTENSION OF HIS HAND...

ALL ARE NOT SO LUCKY, SO THE PETTY CRIMINALS HAVE THEIR NECKS PUT INTO A CRUDE STOCK TO PREVENT ESCAPE EN ROUTE TO THE HOOSEGOW...

SMALL-FRY CRIMINALS ARE TRIED BY THE EVER-AMAZING WITCH DOCTOR, WHO IS A MIRACLE OF DEXTERITY, ACTING AS LAWYER, JURY, AND SENTENCING JUDGE...

.. FINALLY, ONCE INSIDE THE DIRTY CRAMPED CELL, MINOR OFFENDERS ARE SHACKLED AT THE ANKLES, WHILE MAJOR OFFENDERS ARE SHACKLED HAND AND FOOT, AND FORCED TO WEAR A BALL AND CHAIN!

The PEOPLES of AFRICA

ZULU SORCERERS KNOW SECRETS OF TELEPATHY, MIND-READING AND HYPNOSIS THAT HAS PUZZLED MODERN SCIENCE. THEIR MEDICINE MEN ARE EXPERTS AT TREATING TUBERCULOSIS, PNEUMONIA AND *CANCER!* THEIR METHODS HAVE PROVED EFFECTIVE ENOUGH FOR THE JOHANNASBURG WITWATERSRAND UNIVERSITY TO *DEVOTE* A SPECIAL DEPARTMENT TO THE STUDY OF NATIVE MEDICINE, MEDICAMENTS AND SUPERNATURAL PHENOMENON.

ZULU MEDICINE MEN KNEW ABOUT SUBCONSCIOUS REFLEXES, GUILT COMPLEXES AND THE RESULTANT EEFFECTS ON HEART PALPITATIONS AND SWEAT GLANDS, *HUNDREDS OF YEARS* BEFORE NEURO-PSYCHIATRISTS BECAME AWARE OF SUCH FACTS! CRUDE LIE DETECTORS TESTS HAVE BEEN USED SUCCESSFULLY IN ZULULAND FOR CENTURIES. A CIRCLE IS FORMED AROUND THE ACCUSED AND DRUMS BEGIN TO BEAT. WHEN THE FRENZY IS AT ITS MAXIMUM, ORGANIC CHANGES ARE NOTED BY THE MEDICINE MAN, WHO DETECTS THE GUILT IMMEDIATELY BY HEART PALPITATIONS AND THE ODOR OF *PERSPIRATION.*

THE MADUBU OF THE ITURI USE LEOPARD TEETH FOR CURRENCY. EACH TOOTH HAS A SPECIFIC VALUE, THE FANGS THE HIGHEST. HAVING NEITHER POCKETS NOR BANKS, THE MADUBA CARRY THE TEETH ON NECKLACES AND ON THEIR HEAD-DRESS THAT ALL MAY SEE THEIR WEALTH AND IMPORTANCE.

THE STRANGE CUCUMBER SHAPE OF THE MANGBETU HEAD IS ATTAINED BY TIGHTLY WRAPPING AND SHAPING THE SOFT BONES OF THE NEWLY BORN CHILD TO CONFORM TO TRIBAL TRADITION.

THE WAGENIAS CONSTRUCT CANOES THAT CAN CARRY UP TO EIGHTY MEN IN STANDING POSITION. A "COXSWAIN" KEEPS THE OARSMEN IN RHYTHM BY BEATING A TAMBOUR ON THE STERN.

THE ICON TIME FORGOT

One of the most enduring archetypes in all of literature is that of the explorer, the stranger in a strange land. In myth and in popular culture, this theme has been reinvented many times for new audiences—from the voyages of Jason and his Argonauts to the interstellar adventures of *Star Trek's* USS Enterprise.

Placed in between those two extremes is the iconic figure of the African Explorer, based on a group of real-life personages in which legend and fiction intermingled, primarily during the 19th century.

The imagination of the English-speaking world was gripped by the supposed true tales of exploration and adventure in exotic climes, supplied by the likes of Richard Francis Burton and Henry Morton Stanley.

Burton in particular was world famous, definitely known to virtually everyone living in Britain during the mid-to-late 1800s. He provided newspaper and magazine writers with so much material, he almost created a genre unto himself. As

an explorer, soldier of fortune and self-styled cultural anthropologist, Burton penetrated deep into the Middle East and Africa. In 1857 Burton was given credit for discovering Lake Tanganyika and for introducing England to the word "safari".

Although not as flamboyant as Burton, journalist Henry Morton Stanley's dangerous trek deep into the Dark Continent in search of the missing explorer Dr. David Livingstone, supplied even more fodder for scribes the world over. Stanley did indeed find Livingstone, and in the process, created a rhetorical question which is still in use today: "Dr. Livingstone, I presume?"

Stanley also coined the term "the Dark Continent" and took credit for discovering the Congo's Great Falls, which were later named after him. He was also incorrectly named as the discoverer of the Rwenzori Mountains, the legendary Mountains of the Moon.

Like Burton before him, Stanley was knighted by Queen Victoria.

Inevitably, in response to so many

allegedly true accounts of African explorers filling newspapers, magazines and journals, fictional counterparts began appearing, mainly in Penny Dreadfuls and dime novels.

At the same time, mainstream Victorian authors such as Rudyard Kipling, Robert Louis Stevenson and Henry Rider Haggard began laying the groundwork for the genre which became known as adventure literature, and its many sub-categories.

Haggard had an edge over his colleagues in that he actually lived in Africa and was friends with several professional big-game hunters. He combined their traits with that of Burton and Stanley to create Allan Quatermain. Many episodes in the reports of the two men served as loose inspiration for people and places in *King Solomon's Mines*. For example, Stanley's description of the Mountains of the Moon served as the basis of the pass between the peaks called Sheba's Breasts.

King Solomon's Mines and Quatermain were so well-received by the reading public that Haggard wrote many prequels and sequels...thirteen novels and handful of shorter works featuring the character and his milieu over the following 30 years.

Quatermain became the template for all explorer-adventure heroes which followed throughout the late 19th and 20th centuries,

influencing characters as diverse as Tarzan, Conan and Doc Savage.

It was not long after the publication of the novel in 1885 that *King Solomon's Mines* was adapted to other media, beginning with a stage play in London in the 1890s, and in 1918, a silent movie filmed on location in South Africa. The movie is considered lost, with only a few stills of the cast still in existence.

In 1937, a much more ambitious movie version of the novel was released. Starring

Cedric Hardwicke as Quatermain, much of it was filmed in Africa. Although well-received at the time, the movie is mainly notable for casting charismatic black actor and singer Paul Robeson as Umbopa/Prince Ignosa, who played a central role in

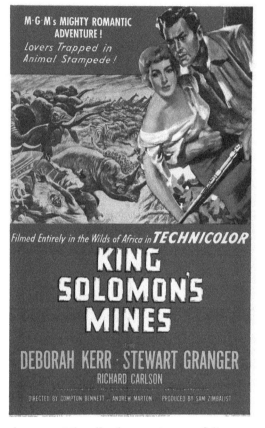

the story. Like all other versions to follow, a white woman character was created out of whole cloth and added to the story to serve as a love interest.

A big-budget Technicolor epic was released in 1950, starring Stewart Granger as Quatermain and Debra Kerr as another white female love interest. Like its predecessor, *King Solomon's Mines* was filmed mainly in Africa, with a number of Watusi tribespeople as extras. Unlike its predecessor, the character of Umbopa (although played by a Watusi actor) was greatly reduced. The movie was very successful, the second-

highest grossing movie of the year in the US.

Nine years later, a low-budget sequel entitled *Watusi* was released, starring George Montgomery as Harry Quatermain, son of Allan. The film relied heavily on footage from the 1950 movie and barely made its costs back at the box office.

Allan Quatermain did not appear in a film again until 1979's *King Solomon's Treasure,* which combined elements of the first and second Quatermain novels. Despite a veteran cast (including Patrick McNee and David McCallum) and being filmed on location in

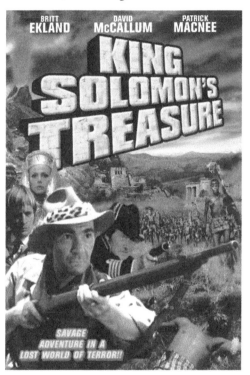

Swaziland, the film had very limited release. Casting John Colicos as Quatermain, known mainly as Kor, the first Klingon commander on *Star Trek* and the scheming Baltar on *Battlestar Galactica,* was an odd choice.

Due to the success of the global blockbuster, *Raiders of The Lost Ark* in 1981 and its sequel *Indiana Jones and the Temple of Doom* (1984), studios scrambled to come up with their own versions. Cannon Films decided to return to the source material for Jones and released *King Solomon's Mines* in 1985, starring Richard Chamberlin as Quatermain

and Sharon Stone as romantic interest Jesse Huston. As a marketing ploy, the film was released 100 years to the day of the novel's publication date.

A second film starring the Chamberlin/Stone duo was filmed back-to-back and released in 1986. Entitled *Allan Quatermain and the Lost City of Gold,* it did not perform as well as KSM and plans for a Quatermain franchise were shelved.

A movie entitled *High Adventure* and purporting to tell the adventures of Chris Quatermain (Allan's grandson) received limited European release in 2001 and was reportedly made to cash in on the success of 1999's period piece, *The Mummy.*

In 2003 Quatermain returned in the person of Sean Connery as the central char-

acter in *League of Extraordinary Gentlemen,* based on the comic series by Alan Moore and Kevin O'Neil. Although blessed with a

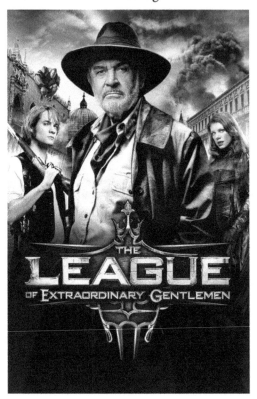

big budget, the film received largely negative reviews. It's interesting to note that as Quatermain was an influence on Indiana Jones, Sir Sean had played Indy's father in the third Jones film.

Hallmark Channel's *King Solomon's Mines* (2004) cast Patrick Swayze as an American Allan Quatermain adventuring across Africa, this time with Allison Doody as the prerequisite

white female interest. Ms Doody was Indiana Jones (and his father's) love interest in *Indiana Jones and the Last Crusade* (1988).

The notoriously low-budget Asylum Films produced *Allan Quatermain and the Temple of Skulls* in 2008 , attempting to cash-in on that year's *Indiana Jones and the Kingdom of The Crystal Skull.* With a very limited budget and cast, it also received a limited release.

Although Indiana Jones is the most well-known adventurer cast in the Quatermain mould, two characters from the Golden Age of Comics had successful runs as movie heroes.

Jungle Jim Bradley got his start in a newspaper comic strip of the same name in 1934, created by the legendary Alex Raymond. After a successful stint in radio, Jungle Jim

prised of 16 films. The movies and a later TV series starred former Tarzan Johnny Weissmuller as the eponymous jungle hero.

Congo Bill was a DC Comics adventurer, very reminiscent of Jungle Jim. He starred in his own serial in 1948

Even real-life showmen and animal trappers such as Clyde Beatty and Frank "Bring

starred in a 12-part serial and in 1948 as the title character of a movie franchise, com-

'Em Back Alive" Buck were reframed as Quatermainesque adventure heroes in serials and comic books throughout the 1930s and 40s.

Over the last decade, there seemed to be little that could be done with Allan Quatermain and his setting of 19th century Africa. As iconic as the archetype of the fearless African Explorer once was, it had lost its romantic lustre and become associated with the much darker figure of the Colonizer, the Exploiter. Quatermain and his many imitators were in danger of being forgotten.

On a personal level, I loved the African Adventure genre so much, I even wrote my

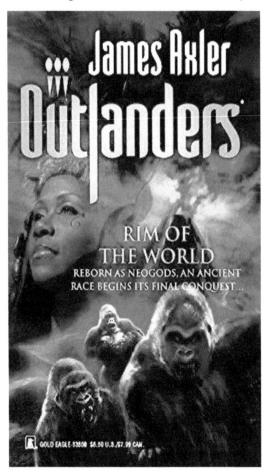

own contribution: *Rim of the World,* the 37th entry in my *Outlanders* novel series, written under my "James Axler" pen-name.

Considering this, when I was first approached

to work with Pablo Marcos on a graphic novel adaptation of *King Solomon's Mines,* I was very enthusiastic—primarily because of

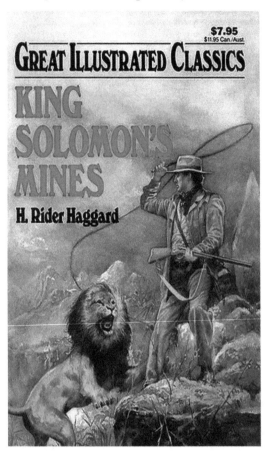

the opportunity to work with Pablo, who rightly deserves the appellation of "legendary" due to his incredible body of work.

Several years before, Pablo had illustrated a children's edition of *King Solomon's Mines,* and I knew it was one of his favourite stories. I did a quick re-read of Haggard's original novel and my enthusiasm inched down from its peak a bit. The structure of the book is sprawling and is often ponderously paced. Due to its length, a literal adaptation was out of the question.

I determined it was best to streamline the story and reimagine some of the characters—particularly Quatermain. In the novel, he is presented as a short, wiry man in his 50s.

Younger male characters actually did most of the heavy lifting. I decided to shave off a few years (and his beard) and present him as much more physically active.

Since all of the film versions took major liberties with the storyline, I didn't feel we would disrespect the spirit of the original novel by doing the same. But rather than

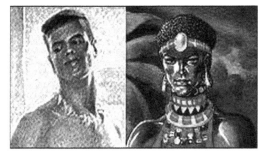

follow the well-travelled route of creating a white woman romantic interest, I took Prince Ignosi, who in the guise of Umbopa, acted as a guide for Quatermain's safari, and created the beautiful Princess Ignosa...a twist which had never been done in any of the other adaptations.

I also felt that mysticism needed to play a larger role, inasmuch as the legends of King Solomon associated him with all manner of magical artefacts and weapons, from killer thrones to enchanted rings and swords.

I suggested making these changes to Pablo and he was not only very enthusiastic but had ideas of his own, such as adding Gajeema, Ignosa's cheetah companion to the mix. We also agreed to downplay Quatermain's role as a big-game hunter. This wasn't

difficult, since even in the book, the expedition was to find a missing man, not collect trophies.

The process of creating the first edition of the *King Solomon's Mines* graphic novel was fraught with delays. The agreement with the first publisher was cancelled and for a time, it appeared the project would never be completed.

Fortunately, Stephen Friedt rode over the hill to the rescue. *King Solomon's Mines* would not have been completed without his timely involvement and we are forever grateful for that.

For this edition, we took the opportunity to correct some production problems and enhance the art. We also expanded the book with value-added features, such as classic educational and historical pieces that had not seen print in well over fifty years. Although they help to put *King Solomon's Mines* within a larger cultural context, they must be viewed through the lens of the time period in which they were originally created.

Collaborating with Pablo Marcos and book designer Melissa Martin Ellis has been one of the most enjoyable experiences of my career as a professional creator.

I'd love to do it all over again. Since the Classics Reimagined imprint was created with the idea of re-imagining other classic works as graphic novels, such as Sir Arthur Conan Doyle's *The Lost World* and Haggard's own *She,* there are plenty of possibilities!

Mark Ellis,
County Cork, Ireland,
April, 2022

H.R. HAGGARD

The mid-Victorian era was a period of colonization and industrial progress. During this time, the romantic adventure novel had its greatest popularity.

From this school of writing came countless numbers of stories which were written primarily to provide the reader with entertainment. While most of these works have long passed into oblivion, those by Sir Henry Henry Rider Haggard are still widely read today. His vivid imagination and ability make the reader accept the incredible made Haggard's novels live through many generations of readers.

H. Rider Haggard was born June 22, 1856, at Bradenham Hall, Norfolk, England. He received a good education and while at school, developed an interest in literature and writing. Before he had any stories published, however, he moved to Natal, South Africa as secretary to the governor. Soon afterward he became Maser and Registrar of the High Court in Transvaal. Five years later, he returned to England. With him were the memories and impression dark and mysterious Africa.

Haggard studied law and was admitted to the bar in 1884. However, the very year he became a lawyer, he score popular with his novel, Dawn. In 1885, he wrote *The Witches Head* and in 1886, *King Solomon's Mines*, the plot of which was suggested by the ruins of Zimbabwe. With such a flow of fiction, Haggard could not devote much time to legal work. As a result, his law practice slowly dwindled.

Haggard's mental energies were concentrated on writing but he soon became restless. He found that writing alone could not give him complete satisfaction in living. Too often, his brain bogged down when it was overworked and ideas that seemed good in conception failed in execution. He searched for other outlets for his energies.

It could not be other mental work but some physical way to release energy that would leave his mind free to absorb and develop ideas that would shine forth as creative literature. Haggard turned toward farming. For many years, he pursued to widely different occupations and interests—fiction and agriculture.

Such a course of living proved highly satisfactory and profitable in many ways. Haggard's experiments in farming gave him material for another kind of writing which took the form of *The Farmer's Yearbook* in 1899 and *Rural England* in 1902. These two works dealt with matters quite important to English farmers and were the result of a study which took two full yars to complete.

In addition, Haggard wrote *The Poor and the Land* in 1905 which was the report of an inquiry into colonial land settlement in Great Britain.

Fiction, however, was Haggard's greatest gift and for which he is the most remembered. He was the successful author in such other fields as historical and analytical as well as the fantastic.

In recognition of H. Rider Haggard's many accomplishments in writing and also for his welfare work throughout Great Britain, the author was knighted by the Crown in 1912. He lived a full and interesting life until his death on May 14, 1925.

CREATOR'S BIOGRAPHIES

PABLO MARCOS

is an internationally celebrated comic book artist and commercial illustrator, best known his work on such popular American comics characters as Batman , Spider-Man, The Avengers and Conan The Barbarian. During the 1970s his signature character was Marvel Comics' the Zombie, for which Pablo drew all but one story in the black-and-white horror-comics magazine *Tales of the Zombie*.

Throughout the 1990s, Pablo and his studio produced many books in Waldman Publishing's Great Illustrated Classics series of young adult adaptations of *Gulliver's Travels*, *Journey to the Centre of The Earth* and *King Solomon's Mines*.

Pablo is the artist on *The Army of Darkness*, *Red Sonja*, and *Savage Tales* series from Dynamite Entertainment.

www.PabloMarcosart.com

MARK ELLIS

is a prolific novelist and comics creator whose many credentials include *Doc Savage*, *The Wild Wild West*, *Mack Bolan*, *Deathlands*, *The Justice Machine*, and *The Man From U.N.C.L.E.* among others.

In 1996 he created the best-selling *Outlanders* novel series for Harlequin Enterprise's Gold Eagle imprint, writing under the pen name of James Axler. *Outlanders* is the most successful mass-market paperback series published in the last 30 years. The author of over 50 books, Mark has been featured in *Starlog*, *Comics Scene* and *Fangoria* magazines. He has also been interviewed by Robert Siegel for NPR's *All Things Considered*.

www.MarkEllisInk.com

MELISSA MARTIN ELLIS

is an internationally known photographer, best-selling author and professional graphic designer. The former creative director of Millennium Pubications, her artwork and articles have been featured in numerous exhibits and galleries, as well as in print media such as the *Redwood Review*, *Newport This Week*, *Newport Life Magazine*, *The Boston Globe*, *Horseman's Yankee Peddler* and *Balancing The Tides*.

She is author of *The Everything Guide to Photography, 2nd Ed.* She and her husband Mark Ellis collaborated on *The Everything Guide to Writing Graphic Novels*.

Melissa's *101 Ways To Find A Ghost* and two editions of her *The Everything Ghost Hunting Book* have topped international best-seller lists in the paranormal category for several years.

www.Mellissart.com

Art Direction, Production
& Design
Melissa Martin Ellis

Additional Art
Mike Arens
George Tuska
Maurice Whitman

Special Thanks to
Stephan Friedt

www.markosia.com

Lightning Source UK Ltd.
Milton Keynes UK
UKHW050650290822
408003UK00002B/14